The Mystery of Perfume

Rita Schnitzer

Illustrations by Rosa Batlle

ORBIS · LONDON

Also published in the same series
The Secrets of Herbs

Printed in Spain
ISBN 0-85613-873-8

I am indebted to the following for their collaboration:
Ramón and Francisco Planas from the Museum of Perfume;
Ramón Monegal, Perfumer from the House of Myurgia, and
Rosendo Mateu, Perfumer from the House of Antonio Prig.

Perfume has the power to evoke countless ideas in our imagination: the fragrance of beautiful flowers, the mysticism of religion, the eroticism of One Thousand and One Nights, the sensuality of Dark Africa, the Far East and its hidden secrets. These days, when we press the spray of a bottle of perfume or of cologne, and a cloud appears before our eyes, we cannot imagine what efforts, thousands of years ago, went into extracting secret aromas from Mother Nature, enabling us to use them for their own sake. In this way perfumery was born. For both men and women, perfume has come to be a part of our lives, and has a special value in our relationships. It can unconsciously influence our being attracted to someone or rejecting them; it can create an aura of mystery, change a mood, bring back feelings and memories, arouse passions and change attitudes. We can discover this magic world of bewitching power and enjoy the products of nature, science and art which create those fine, intoxicating fragrances that arouse our dreams of beauty, mystery, and love.

The History of Perfume

Perfume has a history as old as mankind. Man has always valued scents and when we speak of Paradise, we visualize a garden abounding with beautiful flowers and plants with a wealth of fragrance. In the Stone Age, when our forefathers discovered fire and the aromas of burnt wood, their first thought was to offer them to the gods. From altars and temples they sent the smoke of resins and scented woods to the skies in order to please the unknown heavenly powers 'per fumun' – by means of smoke. This ritual gave perfume its name. We find perfume closely tied up with religious ceremonies in all ancient civilizations. We still have the living evidence of this use in the Catholic Church and in the religions of China and India.

The ancient writings of the Sumerians, which have been preserved for more than five thousand years, already refer to perfumes, oils, and ointments. In Egypt a veritable science of perfumery came to be created. Teaching priests the secret art of manufacturing scents was attributed to the god Thoth, under the condition that it was used in his honour alone. These priests who could well be called the first artisan perfumers in the world, had exclusive responsibility for manufacturing richly fragrant substances, and the ingredients they used were a jealously guarded secret.

The perfume which they used was made of various aromatic spices in the form of fine powder. The best way of paying tribute to the gods was to burn it in honour of them. Noah burnt cedar and myrrh to offer thanks for his salvation from the Flood and 'the sweet odour was pleasing to Jehovah'.

The Persians were the first people to manage to produce ointment by soaking flowers in oil and pressing them when the oil had become saturated with their aroma. The ointments, together with scented smoke, were used in religious rites. In the Old Testament, Moses was ordered to mix extracts of the finest myrrh and cinnamon, sweet flag and chinaberry with pure olive oil for the preparation of a sacred balsam. Later, priests were anointed with aromatic ointments, in the same way as emperors, kings and high dignitaries to distinguish them from the common people. Good odours attracted the gods and the more repulsive ones kept them away. Thus, men perfumed themselves with odorous oils and anointed the dead with

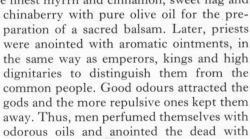

fragrant balsams to help them meet with the clemency of the gods. The Egyptians associated perfume with immortality, and scents had a place of importance during funerals, and were stored in alabaster and glass containers. When the Pharaohs' tombs were discovered, formulas for perfume were found on the walls, and when the ointment jars were opened, after more than two thousand years, they still exuded aromas.

In those times, religious life intertwined with daily life, and perfume gradually acquired a great significance in everyday uses with the priviliged classes. It was used extensively for religious purposes, as well as for social and aesthetic reasons. At banquets, as a token of esteem, it was customary to place scented cones of perfumed fat on the heads of the guests, and these cones would melt slowly. Beautiful youths showered guests with rose water and this is still done today in many Eastern cultures. Liquid perfume too was sprinkled on the head or on the beard. Mary Magdalene anointed the feet of Christ with sweet smelling spikenard and the three Kings adored Him and offered Him gold, incense and myrrh as a sign of his royal and divine nature. Perfume acquired an exalted symbolic value.

Babylonia was, for a long time, the most important garden for aromas in the world. From India and the Persian Gulf came spices, from Arabia odorous gums and from Judea precious balsams.

Perfumes were widely used, with fine cosmetics, principally for the art of seduction. Women anointed themselves with pomades of aromatic herbs

before going to meet their husbands. The Queen of Sheba overwhelmed Solomon with her beauty, enhanced by the seductive quality of her perfumes. Semiramis, creator of the famous hanging gardens of Babylon, had trees with aromatic resins brought from India and Arabia to make perfumes. Nefertiti and Cleopatra, queens of Egypt, reposed on rose-petal couches. Ruth followed the advice of her mother-in-law: 'Wash, perfume yourself and put your best clothes on', before she went to captivate Boaz, the master of the fields where she worked. Judith anointed herself to seduce Holofernes who was laying seige to the city of Betulia.

After the conquests of Alexander the Great, Greece was flooded with the fragrances of Egypt and the East. The Greeks with their great imagination believed perfume to have been divinely conceived by the gods. It is mentioned specifically in their mythology: Hera and the Graces anoint themselves with sweet smelling oils to seduce Zeus.

Women are described as enchantresses in the art of preparing fragrances. They are thought to have magic powers. Circes managed to keep Ulysses from leaving the enchanted island by mixing sweet fragrances and aromatic herbs, which made him lose his senses. Medea returned Jason's youth by bathing him with aromatic herbs.

As in other countries, perfumes were used for cremation; ointments for rubbing into the skin and essences to sprinkle on people, clothes, objects and furniture. For each part of the body there was a special perfume and there were many aromas for different occasions. Wrestlers and athletes would rub special oils into their bodies; at parties, doves would flutter about and from their wings would fall drops of rose-coloured perfumed water. Women and men alike would delight in these aromas which helped them, as they said, enjoy life.

Greek perfumeries were meeting places where politics could be discussed. The Greeks, with their heightened sense of aesthetics, created flasks (many still survive), specially shaped, for ointments, oils and essences.

At the beginning of the Roman Empire, the use of odorous products was limited to religious ceremonies and to the funerals of important people. But it was in the time of Nero and Caligula that extravagant use of perfume began. It is said that, at the funeral of Poppea, Nero wasted more incense than is produced in all of Arabia in one year. At high society parties, fountains of aromas poured forth and when they conducted their famous orgies, sweet smelling resins were burnt and essences sprinkled in the rooms.

The Romans made a name for themselves by inventing new combinations of smells. Pliny, Ovid and Criton have left astonishing accounts on the composition and use of perfumes and cosmetics.

The early Christian church taught the value of asceticism and perfume fell into disuse, as it was considered sinful, because it stimulated the senses. Only good smells were associated with Paradise but men had to refrain from using fragrances so that they would not fall into temptation.

The Arabs continued the practice of the refined art of perfumery. Furthermore, they invented the technique of distillation and they are credited with having produced rose water. Roses, musk and amber were the favourite perfumes of the Arabs and, to this day, all three form a basic part of the luxury perfumes.

The Orient has always appreciated sensual pleasures. Islam was no exception. Mohammed himself put women and fragrances in first place amongst the joys of life. In the world of the harem women immersed themselves in baths of floral essences and anointed themselves with richly scented oils.

Under the influence of the Arabs, Spain acquired a great fascination with flowers, fruits and gardens and, of course, aromas. Spanish perfumery experienced a considerable step forward.

Perfumes were introduced to Europe via Spain and the crusades. The crusaders returned home from the East with their arms full of perfumes and spices. In Europe, daily baths became a regular activity during this period. Soon, men and women were enjoying the aromas of rose, narcissus, saffron, sandalwood, amber and musk. In the south of France the local plants began to be cultivated for their extracts, which were sometimes mixed with substances brought from the East.

Violets, roses and all the floral aromas connected with the flowers from the fields of Provence were the favourites of that time. Bedclothes and other clothes were impregnated with aromatic herbal fragrances.

However, it was not only Asia, Africa and Europe that experienced a great development in the art of perfumery. In the countries of the New World, fragrances are known to have been used in pre-Columbian religious ceremonies.

The travels of the great adventurers Christopher Columbus and Magellan to the New World brought them into contact with new aromas. The attempts to obtain these goods were known as the War of the Spices and lasted for two hundred years. In Italy a phenomenon, along the lines of what happened in other countries took place. The strong sensual perfumes were imported from the East by the Venetian merchants. At the same time, local herbs were grown  in monasteries for the extraction of essences. The true art of perfumery began in the fifteenth century. With the Renaissance men rediscovered sensuality. They freed themselves from mystic ideals, and began once again to enjoy pleasures and learnt once more how to care for, embellish and perfume their bodies. They covered their skin with amber, musk and civet; gloves and similar accessories became part of the gentleman's dress and the glove-maker's trade became synonymous with the perfumer's. The following centuries, the sixteenth and seventeenth,

 came to stand as the Golden Age of perfumes. When Catherine de Medici married Henri II and came to France, the talents of the Italians and the French united to this art's advantage. The city of Grasse, which was originally Arabic, became the centre of French perfumery.

In England, perfumes were used extensively during the reign of Henry VIII.

Henry valued aromas highly and Queen Isabella adored sumptuous clothes and fine perfumes. From this time on, when perfumes were mixed, musk and civet were nearly always used.

During the plague, what was felt to be the therapeutic power of lavender motivated the English towards the end of the 18th century, to take the first steps in making lavender water, which was later to be a completely English speciality – the aroma of the age of Queen Victoria and an 'impressionistic picture of English life', as an English perfumer once said.

At the beginning of the eighteenth century the production of 'Eau de cologne' marked a turning point in the history of perfume. Eau de cologne was refreshing and stimulating.

Later, Napoleon decreed that houses should be numbered and the door of the factory where this perfume was produced in Cologne had the number 4711. This number is still the internationally-known brand of the Mûlhens House, which claims to have produced the cologne from a formula of the Italian Paolo de Feminis. His nephew Juan Maria Farina managed to market his perfume 'Aqua Admirabilis' (especially at the beginning) as a medicinal water because of the cleansing effect of the alcohol. At a time when general hygiene and pharmaceutical industries were needed, this fact was of great importance.

The lively eaux de cologne appeared as a novelty, compared to the other heavy fragrances of the time before the

Rococo period and they soon made their mark. Under Louis XIV France created many famous perfumes; Louis XV's court was known as the 'perfumed court'. Madame de Pompadour, mistress of the king, was particularly fond of fine aromas, and so was Queen Marie Antoinette. She ended up paying for her fancies and love of luxury by dying on the guillotine.

During the Revolution, in spite of the government's prohibitions, perfumes continued to be used, and extravagant excesses, fashionable at the time, are well known. There was even an elixir called 'à la guillotine'. Napoleon Bonaparte was very sensitive to aromas. He carried with himself hundreds of flasks with pomades, scented waters for cleanliness and valuable boxes for aromatic tablets. It is said that he used a litre of 'Aqua Admirabilis' a week and sixty flasks of Spanish essence of jasmine

a month. Josephine, too, loved aromas, and especially moss, which lingered in her residence, Malmaison, a long time after her death.

At the beginning of our century a new age of perfumery began. Scientific and technical progress made new manufacturing methods easier for aromas which contained the first synthetic products, replacing natural essences. These products lowered the cost of the raw materials and chemical processes enriched perfumery with the creation of new bouquets.

Thanks to organic chemistry, fashion and trade, perfumery changed from being artisan to industrial. Today perfumery is a very varied art and embraces different areas of our daily lives, from food to the most refined luxuries. The world of perfumery has developed so much that it has become an essential part of modern man's life. It complements hygiene, good habits and gives a feeling of satisfaction, and has seductive power.

The Creation of Perfume

Perfume is the combination of natural and synthetic odours in an alcohol solution. Perfumery is the art of subtly, precisely and delicately combining these aromatic substances so as to attain a harmonious, homogeneous and long-lasting mixture, which is found to be pleasing. A suggestive, original lingering fragrance is the secret of any good perfume.

Around ten thousand essences form the bases of perfumes, and these can be divided into three groups: vegetable, animal and synthetic. Nature boasts seven hundred to a thousand raw materials. Plants offer almost all their parts: flowers (jasmine, spikenard, rose, tuberose, hyacinth, lavender); leaves (patchouli, tarragon, mint); fruits (lemon, orange, mandarine, bergamot); seeds (coriander, pepper, celery, parsley); roots (vetiver, iris, ginger); woods (cedar and sandalwood); bark (cinnamon); balsams (benzoin, Peruvian

balsam); resins (galbanum, myrrh, opoponax); moss (oak moss, pine moss); and seaweed. There are various methods for extracting the odorous substances from plants: distillation by vapour, the extraction of soluble, volatile substances and pressing the fruits. The most up-to-date method is extraction using solvents which results in a wax-like solid product being formed, which is very aromatic. It is mixed with alcohol, filtered and kept frozen. The alcohol is continually evaporated until the absolute is obtained, the purest form of the perfume.

The natural raw materials are very costly, especially because great quantities of the best quality are needed to obtain the essence. To make a gram of absolute essence of jasmine, for example, five thousand flowers are needed, each one carefully picked by hand. The natural essence of jasmine consists of six hundred different chemicals of different volatility.

Animal essences used in perfumes are musk, ambergris castor and civet.

Musk is a secretion produced by the male musk deer when it is in season. The deer lives in the mountains of the Himalayas and Tibet. The aromatic substance is extracted from the dried, easily crushed gland – oily, bitter and reddish brown in colour – that is found in the sheath of the male sexual

organ. Authentic musk is thought to be the most expensive substance of perfumery, and dealers have been known to substitute other substances for it. Nowadays, musk deer are bred in captivity for their musk secretions. However, musk is being used less and less in  perfumery because of the difficulty and costs involved and also because of the arrival of chemical substances artificially derived from musk, the main odour of the animal's gland. Another cheaper kind of musk is also used which is produced from the musk rat of North America.

Ambergris is an opaque substance produced in the spermwhale's abdomen. The spermwhale is found in the coastal waters off Asia and Africa in the Indian Ocean and ambergris appears floating on the water or deposited on beaches, although it has become scarcer because of the decline in the whale population. Its velvety, balsamy odour is also associated with the skin and helps to fix perfumes because of its quality as a fixative.

Castor comes from a kind of beaver whose habitat is in Siberia and Canada. Castor, or castoreum as it is also called, is the strong-smelling secretion of the anal glands and plays a part in the sexual attraction of the animals. Civet is a butter-like secretion produced by the civet cat, which lives in parts of north Africa. Its smell is strong and repugnant and is only pleasant when very diluted. It is used in infusion form to perfect and enrich great perfumes. It is clear that all these animal products can be linked to the sexual drive of the male and female. To them belong erotic qualities which strengthen attraction and which bestow an aura of mystery and fantasy to the person who is using it. The perfumer values these essences highly so as to manufacture penetrating, lasting and warm perfumes.

Finally, synthetic essences – man-made products – resulting from research and chemical synthesis abound in most of today's perfumes. The development of perfumery is the result of some 9,000 chemicals which have enriched it incredibly. When these processes were discovered it was thought they would be used only to reproduce natural odours, as these can vary from one place to another and, furthermore, natural raw materials are often found in distant, and possibly warring countries. The synthetic products, however, have the advantage of bringing continuity. Today they complement natural essences and are not only a simple substitute which costs less. The quality of perfume demands the combination of natural bases and chemical substances. Moreover, bouquets have been invented which do not exist naturally and revolutionary new perfumes have been created. Two of the pioneering chemists responsible for these products, Paul Sabatier and Victor Grignare, were awarded the Nobel Prize for chemistry in 1912. Creating a perfume is a delicate art. It is the result of total artistic and professional dedication. The perfumer must have a deep knowledge of the thousands of products with a distinctive odour, an excellent memory for smells, and most of all, the imagination to combine them so as to produce the required effects. In the whole world there are no more than a few thousand people endowed with a special olfactory sensitivity, that is to say, a natural, developed talent. These artists, called 'the Nose', are composers of fragrances, artists of smell and air, creators of new perfumes, latter-day alchemists. A true composer of perfumes keeps aromas and formulas imprinted on his mind. This is why there have been artists who have composed great perfumes even after having lost their sense of smell like Beethoven, who

remembered chords and composed music from memory, after he had become deaf. The creation of a perfume is comparable to the composition of a musical score or a painting.

An idea, a feeling, an emotion, or an event can inspire a composition. Thus, the starting point for an artist is not the sense of smell, but his brain. Creating a perfume is a slow and complex process. The possible combinations are infinite and at the discretion of the individual artist's taste. Hundreds and thousands of different tests are needed along the various stages of evaporation, and these tests are conducted on different people, in different conditions. Creating a perfume can take a year or several years of work.

Inspiration is not the only important factor; the chords, the basic materials, must form a harmonious unity. The development of an odour, the gradual dissolution of the substances, can be seen to have three stages. The structure of a perfume is based on three points, or to speak in musical terms, its structure can be defined in three levels: top notes, which are perceived in the first moments of smelling a perfume; middle notes, which form the body, the heart of the bouquet, and determine the theme of the perfume; and bottom notes, which stay in the mind. The top notes must correspond to the volatile products normally obtained from citrus fruits, such as lemon and orange. The middle substances, like flowers, spices, rosemary

and thyme, give body and blend with the strong and persistent odours of the bass notes. These bottom, or bass, notes are woods, moss, pachouli, iris, vanilla, vetiver, animal notes and aldehydes (chemical products with heavy notes, both citrus and floral). They are not very volatile, because they must last and fix the body of the perfume. Every note alters with the addition of other notes, which have an important part to play in the composition, creating original aromas with distinctive personalities which will remain imprinted on people's minds. Musk and amber, for example, have a repulsive smell in their unrefined state, but exude a voluptuous, sensual fragrance when they are blended with other secondary odours.

The perfumer's art is to achieve a perfect combination of all these different notes and chords. A perfume cannot on the one hand evoke fresh green fields at the beginning, and then on the other transport us to the East when we scent the bottom notes. Surprises there may be: some brief discords

to accentuate contrasts. The theme, however, must not change; it is vital that harmony always reigns.

After the alcohol solution is obtained, maceration begins.

The extract, or perfume, is the most concentrated and long-lasting of the liquid fragrances and contains the maximum quantity of pure essence, suspended in alcohol. Just a few drops suffice for the odour to persist for four to eight hours.

Eau de parfum is a little sweeter than perfume. The amount of concentrated ingredients is half that of extract. The effect is accordingly less lasting.

Eau de toilette is less perfumed than Eau de parfum.

Eau fraîche has the same structure as Eau de toilette, but with a fragrance which is defined as citrus-floral-bitter.

Eau de cologne is the lightest form of perfume, with the least amount of oils of essence. It fixes itself least, lasting only a while, but it is also the most refreshing. Perfumes can be grouped into families with common components:

1. *Eaux de colognes* Compositions of citric essences (lemon, orange, bergamot etc.) and orange blossom or nerols. They are refreshing and invigorating, with various lower tones, but generally musky or amber-like.

2. *Eaux fraîches* Natural creations of a citric, fresh quality, but can be altered at the middle and lower tones by different chords (floral, aromatic, bitter, spices, etc.), which give it a fixing quality and character.

3. *Lavender waters* The odour of lavender is reproduced, with lower tones that are complex and lasting.

4. *Woody-country* A family of perfumes composed from a blend of the lavender chord with other herbal-country-woody notes (sage, pine needles, lavender) and their bottom notes of wood and spices, which make them more complex. They are usually masculine smells.

5. *Fern (fougère)* This odour derives from the woods. A chord of lavender, moss, oak, tonka beans and geranium, modified by different notes which give character to these compositions. They are also masculine.

6. *Aromatic* Family born of various chords of aromatic herbs (aniseed, fennel, rosemary, thyme). Recently created masculine notes.

7. *Bitter* Often found in perfumes is this trait, with a smell of cedar, sandalwood as part of the accompaniment of the bass. In fragrances for the male the dominant character of the wood note asserts itself, whether it is simple or complex.

8. *Spices* Its main trait is found in the warm, sweet note of different spices (clove, pepper, cinnamon, vanilla, etc.).

9. *Green* Created on the theme of green, influenced by the chypre and floral families; with a wood-plant smell, with a bouquet of bush, or mown grass. They are fresh, clean, dry, natural and invigorating fragrances. It is one of the most recently developed families.

10. *Floral* A family with the theme of a single flower (lily of the valley, jasmine, rose, etc.)

11. *Florid* Mixture of different flower scents.

a. Florid warm: here the florid character is laced with warm notes in the heart of the perfume, fixed with a base of great volume.

b. Florid-fresh: florid character modified with fresh, less voluminous and sparkling notes which are nonetheless very lively.

12. *Aldehydic* These are florid notes strongly altered by chemical substances known as alifatic aldehydes. These powerful substances, which revolutionized perfumery, are still vital in the creation of new products.

13. *Chypre* 'Eau de chypre' has been known for many centuries and was prepared in Cyprus. It is a combination of oak moss, amber, rose, bergamot and other bitter spices, hide, musk and storax (a resinous tree balsam). They are very lingering and popular perfumes.

14. *Oriental* This family derives from the smells from the Far East, such as cinnamon, vanilla, opoponax etc. They are warm lasting and a little sweet.

15. *Hide and tobacco* Tobacco is a mixture of bitter notes with balsam, powdery and mellow notes. This chord is added to animal, tarry, smoked notes and gives the smell of hide. These perfumes are very forceful, and have personality and duration. They are usually considered masculine notes, but women also use them.

The Erotic Power of Perfume

The end result of fragrances is the delectation of one of our most sensitive senses and one which is the most far removed from reason – the sense of smell. Through it we perceive an infinite number of feelings, many unconsciously, which influence the way we act. The effect of perfumes is highly personal. The same aroma can arouse different feelings and reactions, and can stay with us for a life time. Fragrances have a more penetrating effect than sensations of touch, taste and sight. Every smell causes us to react. A certain aroma immediately evokes a vision in our minds, which can recall thousands of distinct odours from past experiences in our lives. There are smells which evoke moments of child-hood, the family home, school, holidays, the wood, the fields, the sea . . .

However, in addition to this power of evocation and this feeling of living with perfumes, perfumes possess the power to seduce. Perfume is a living thing, envelops our bodies, soothes the skin, and speaks of love. Smell is a call to love. The particular smells of spices have the power to attract or

repel. Have you ever noticed that all the natural elements used in making perfume, vegetable and animal are directly linked to the realm of sexuality? At the height of their splendour, flowers are at their most fragrant so that they can attract insects and ensure their procreation. This is why they produce the most valuable essences for perfumery.

Poets everywhere, and at all times, have sung of the erotic effect of the sensual fragrances of flowers, such as the rose, the orchid, the tuberose or jasmine. The psychological explanation of this is to be found in the fact that many flowers not only give rise to intense emotions, but they are also models in poetry and folklore which symbolize love and beauty.

Woman has always been compared to flowers. A flower in full bloom means ready to love. Something that grows secretly asks to be discovered. To pluck the leaves of a flower, means to rob someone of innocence and wilting flowers represent a dying love. This tender symbolism has found expression in many traditional stories and songs. The language of flowers was used to woo, and also by those with a great sense of modesty.

The refreshing qualities of a perfume, which usually constitutes the top notes, attempt to arouse sleeping, disinterested feelings and to prepare them for real enjoyment of the sense of smell. Inebriating elements, such as the rose, the tuberose, the jasmine or the sunflower,

aim to put the conscience to sleep by intoxicating it, estranging cold reason and manage to silence, for a moment, inhibitions and, in this way, open the way to emotions and imagination.

Erotic fragrances, based on animal products, take full advantage of this power obtained by the refreshing and almost narcotic substances, in a form which slightly resembles the smell of skin, and stimulates sexual fantasies. The stimulating elements, from vanilla, excite the inflamed mind, causing it to perceive everything as sensual.

Animal substances offer the greatest interest, because they are wrapped in a cloud of mystery; they derive from excretions and secretions and all are related to sexual drive, some closely. When they are used in fine combinations they make seductive fragrances. Something in animal carnality survives in them and they exude an excited breath of sexuality, their heavy sweetness being difficult to define. The soft, tender, warm, balsam-like smell of ambergris, the diluted aroma of sweet nut and bitter-animal scent of musk, are smells which recall the human body. Its smell lasts for a long time, and gives the added attraction which is called the 'life' of a perfume. No good synthetic smell can replace an authentic essence. There seems to be a real secret, some subconscious link between the nature of man and

animals – a deep bond between eroticism and aromas. The smell of men
and women becomes more intense
when desire is sparked off, and the
mutual attraction increases. Rasputin
is said to have had a strong animal
odour because of which he managed to influence and attract
women. When man learnt to use fragrances, he attempted
to make himself more attractive using odours similar to his
body's, and animal essences were the first to be used.
Sweet-smelling aromas were part of the sexual ritual of the
most ancient civilizations.

Perfume endeavours, above all, to exalt the beauty of a
woman. Great perfumes are especially sensual and voluptuous. An Italian perfumer once said: 'A perfume is an
abstract presence . . . it is the presence which precedes a
woman before she arrives and what is left after she has
gone. It is what you imagine her to be before you get to
know her, and what you continue to smell beside you when
she herself has vanished.'

How to Choose a Perfume

A woman today has access to a wide range of many different perfumes. It is important to know how to choose your perfume, so that it makes an impression which others will associate with your character and will remind them of you. A perfume may appeal to you because of its affinities with your character or because of its contrast, because of your state of mind, the time of year and even time of day. There

are women who hide behind rather aggressive perfumes; there are others who are more original and natural and who are looking for a delicate aroma, a shade which underlines their personality elegantly and discreetly. A meek woman, a dreamer, or a sentimental type, will not choose the same perfume as a woman who is self-confident, energetic and daring. Certain aromas seem to be more suitable than others for different temperaments. Fresh and green fragrances could be said to be generally more appropriate for young people, while stronger perfumes were more suitable for older people. It is often said that there are perfumes for blondes and others for brunettes. However, the natural colour of the hair is only important in relation to the smell of the skin. So, red-heads usually have a smell which is stronger than blondes and have to use dry, spicy and bitter perfumes, avoiding sweet and sensual fragrances. The latter, made from musk, amber, civet, tobacco, incense and roses are much more suited to the skin of a woman with dark hair; fair-skinned blondes would be better with fresh, light stimulating fragrances. There are, though, no rules. Choose a perfume which suits your personality, and any circumstances. You, yourself, have to let your feelings and instincts guide you in determining a perfume. To do this, you have to be aware of your character, or of the image you want to give. Your perfume and you will have to be in perfect harmony.

As one great perfumer suggests, you should smell the  perfume you are going to wear tomorrow, before eating, when the sense of smell is more sensitive. Don't make the mistake of wearing three or four perfumes at once, and don't try on different perfumes starting with the lightest. Different perfumes can be confused and not appreciated when you are trying them all together. Don't smell the perfume directly from the flask. Put a drop on your skin, preferably on the back of the hand, just inside the wrist or on the inside of the elbow. Don't rub it, this damages the perfume. Don't bring your nose too close to the skin; a perfume should be sensed from a distance. Give it time to adapt to your skin, its acidity and warmth. Perfume unfolds its odour individually with each person using it, on contact with the skin, like a living web which reacts to any changes from within or without. Sometimes the perfume turns sour, because it does not fit in with the skin. Floral and citric perfumes usually change, nearly always for the worse, with very acidic skin. No two bottles of the same perfume smell exactly alike because the oil of the perfume mixes with the oil of your skin and the result is unique. A pleasant perfume on the skin of a friend may be disastrous on your skin. When you have found a perfume that is right for you, when it captivates you and blends perfectly with your skin, then buy that one. But remember that it must please not only you but the people you want to be near you.

How to Use Perfume

Perfume, which is the last touch to hygiene and preparation, complementing your personality and making you feel good, should be applied in small amounts to pulse points, parts of the body where the veins are close to the skin. A hint on the neck, bottom and back of the neck, in the folds of the elbows, on the knees (take care not to apply anything to the middle bits, as they cannot stand perfume), ankles and wrists, shoulders and on the earlobe. Put some on your hair as well, as this spreads fragrances very well, but not on your face, where it is changed by your own smell. The best way of applying the perfume is by spray, avoiding the triangle formed by the nose and shoulders, and before getting dressed, because the drops of perfume can damage and stain your clothes and jewellery. The perfume is dispelled by the heat of the body, and in the most effective and agreeable way on a clean body.

If you are thinking of sunbathing, make sure not to put on perfume, or cologne because some colognes leave stains on the skin.

If you have chosen a strong, rich perfume

with oriental aromas, because you feel mysterious and passionate, keep it for the night. Different occasions require different perfumes. It is a detail of taste, selecting them according to the circumstances.

The next day, after having a shower, it is advisable to use a light, fresh perfume, or a cologne, the lightest, most refreshing and volatile kind of perfume. For the evening you can use a more sophisticated, more brilliant perfume, but never too strong. A perfume must emanate a smooth aroma and not an aggressive odour.

Perfume is even more stimulating, if the same one is not always used, year after year. It can and must change. Experimenting with aromas is interesting, even daring to mix different ones and obtaining a very personal mixture.

Fragrances vary with the seasons of the year. Spring and summer is the time of natural aromas – fresh clean, floral notes, green but dry, in harmony with outdoor life and sport. Autumn and winter are weaker, exotic and sensual fragrances. Climate and atmosphere also affect a perfume. In a warm country, at low altitude, the same aroma spreads more quickly, and dries up earlier, giving the impression of being stronger and sweeter than in colder climes, at higher levels, where it becomes concentrated and slowly evaporates.

Around the sea, spice- and animal-based essences, such as musk, amber or pepper are strong and lasting, while floral and herbal notes spread better in

fields. Eating habits are another factor which affects perfume. Garlic, for example, is certainly a wholesome spice, but is lethal when used with perfume because its strong smell mixes with our favourite fragrance with unpleasant results.

Women smokers should carefully try to adapt their perfume to the smell of tobacco, which changes the chemical composition of the skin and its reaction, reducing the lingering quality of the perfume.

Medicines can also change skin reaction in the same way as they affect the body's metabolism.

Finally, we have to take into account the fact that polluted atmospheres overwhelm perfume. Thus, it is suggested that in cities you apply perfume more generously and more frequently than in the country. Air conditioning is perfume's worst enemy – it absorbs it in no time at all.

Modern perfumes are lighter than the Orient's and evaporate more easily. A good perfume can last from four to eight hours. To achieve a more lasting perfume, you can anoint your wrists with a mineral oil and then apply the perfume over it. You can also help by throwing a few drops of perfume into the bath-water and mixing it with unperfumed baby oil. You can also perfume your underclothes, sweaters, handkerchiefs and hems. The most effective way is to apply the perfume again after four hours.

A perfume demands some care to make it last. Never buy a perfume which has been on display in the shop and never leave it out of its box. Time ages perfume and makes it change. Use it within a year of opening the bottle. For the fragrance to remain intact and not to evaporate, you will have to keep the bottle closed. And above all, avoid change in temperature. Never leave the perfume in direct sunlight or under a fluorescent light. Keep it in a fresh, dark place on a wardrobe shelf or in a box and, in summer, in the lower part of the fridge. Your perfume will appreciate it and will repay you with its unchanging friendship.

Perfumes for Men

King David perfumed his clothes with myrrh, cassia leaf
and aloes to please his princesses. Xerxes, Caesar, Hannibal,
Mark Antony and Genghis Khan, to name but a few,
exuded perfume. Alexander the Great found in the war
tent of Darius, the defeated king of the Persians, vessels
full of odorous pomades and was not ashamed to use them
in his campaigns. The Roman legionnaires anointed their
heads with aromas, in the same way as the Japanese samurai.
These warriors were supposed to be able to recognize the
social rank of their adversaries by the aromas they had.
There were three classes of perfumes: the most sumptuous
for kings, governors, judges and high dignitaries. The
aromas of lesser value belonged to officials, and the third
category to soldiers, merchants and other people.

The great seducers, Brummel, Casanova, Richelieu and
Don Juan, all wore perfume.

King Louis XV of France was widely considered the
sweetest-perfumed monarch of all time. Cavaliers used the

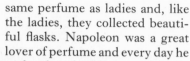

same perfume as ladies and, like the ladies, they collected beautiful flasks. Napoleon was a great lover of perfume and every day he sprinkled two bottles of cologne on his body after his bath. He tended his hands with aromatic creams and never forgot his perfume or gloves, not even during times of war.

There have been national differences in the use of perfumes by men. The Latins have always liked to wear perfume. In the past Germans and English have rejected its use, while the French have preferred to use it discreetly.

Perfumes on men were associated for some time with lack of virility; from the beginning of this century, however, the great Houses of Perfumery launched special perfumes for men. Lavender, and especially hide and tobacco smells – stables, saddles, gunpowder smoke, wood – were considered particularly virile. If in the old times, a woman was told that to conquer a man she had to do it using fragrances, now men were being told that smell counted in their success. The prejudice with which perfume was viewed by most men was overcome, and the field of masculine perfumery of our times began to flourish. Perfume has been added to all men's toiletries: hair and shaving lotions, talcs,

soaps, deodorants, bath gels and creams for skin care. Man had acquired his line in perfumes.

Today perfumes are an indispensable part of getting ready for millions of men and women. Obviously men have to care for their bodies, too, and what they regularly use has a pleasant smell and has come to be justifiably necessary for the sake of his sense of the aesthetic. If it is a virile smell, the women also like it. She, of course, prefers a man with a discreet perfumed smell to one who smells of garlic, onions, beer or wine.

There is a great number of perfumes for men and not all have rustic associations, smelling of burnt gunpowder, or stables; they have developed and are an elegant addition to the cultured man. There are warm, dry and fresh aromas, with notes that are spicy, herby or smell of hide, tobacco, moss, wood, pine, lavender, juniper, vetiver, sandalwood, bergamot and also musk. The typically virile odours still exist but there is a tendency with the modern youth for unisex perfumes. Men's and women's tastes have more in common now, together with habits and fashion, so girls tend to use male aromas. Some perfumeries have launched a perfume for everyone, specially adapted for the youth's own fashion which is becoming ever more similar.

The Language of Perfumes

Nowadays, perfume has almost entirely lost its meaning in ceremonies and religion; but from an aesthetic point of view it has become more and more important. Today, practically no one would consider being ready to go out without the addition of a fragrance in tune with clothing and with the mood of the moment.

Perfumes are deeply related to our emotional lives. The

language of perfume reinforces personalities and heightens the feeling of attraction, suggests social status, expresses states of mind and reveals a particular kind of imagination. Women, above all, feel that the effect of perfume is a stimulant to feelings: if they are happy, the scent will increase their happiness; if they are down at heart, it will console them, stir them to look on the brighter side of things and restore their confidence. If they are in better form, it will make them feel even more balanced, more concerned about their appearance, prettier and more attractive. A woman perfumes herself to please, to express herself, to project a certain image of herself, sometimes to hide her person-  ality, to seduce, to make her presence linger in other people's minds. The scent she chooses, the way she uses the perfume, allow us to glimpse traits of her personality. Perfume is a message, which invites, but it can also lie.

There are perfumes which are light and stimulating, warm and cold, sweet and bitter. Fragrances can be fresh, joyful, quiet, discreet, dynamic, aggressive, distinguished, provocative and sensual. A fresh, citrus aroma is especially suitable for young people. A sweet fragrance with floral notes appears to be more fitting for women with a gentle and romantic look. An oriental perfume is right for mysteri- ous and sensual women. A fragrance of herbs, such as lavender, evokes tranquillity and suits a mature woman. Wood scents suit men of the world and independent women, with initiative and self-confidence. Notes of hide set the standard for masculine aromas.

Are you young? You should use natural waters, which have a citrus tone and which are flowery fresh. They will enhance your charm and will be appreciated by anyone who is frank and uncomplicated. Such a person will later avoid sweet, heavy perfumes, which will clash with his or her nature.

Girl

Alada (Myrurgia)
Azur (Puig)
Colonia Pyn's (Parera)
Eau de Cologne (Hermès)
Eau Jeune (L'Oréal)
1916 (Myrurgia)
4711 (4711)
Royale Ambrée (Legrain)
Vereda (Parera)

Boy

Agua Lavanda Puig (Puig)
Colonia Pyn's (Parera)
Chispas (Dana)
Herbíssimo (Dana)
1916 (Myrurgia)
4711 (4711)

For those who love sport and outdoor life, fresh, citric and herbal fragrances are the most appropriate. The combinations of the smells of leaves, moss, earth, and turf suggest the open air. Men will also appreciate notes of the sea.

Women

Amazone (Hermès)
Cristalle (Chanel)
Eau Verte (Puig)
Eau Vive (Carven)
Ghe (Gherardini)
Ô de Lancôme (Lancôme)
Sport (Coty)
Sportif (Avon)
Sport Scent for Women (Jovan)
Trophée Lancôme (Lancôme)
Vereda (Parera)

Men

Bomber (Adam)
Captain (Molyneux)
Herbal for Men (Shulton)
Ice Blue Cologne (Williams)
Lacoste (Patou)
Men's Club 52 (Rubinstein)
Motor Racing (Segura)
Prime Minister (Parera)
Signoricci 2 (Nina Ricci)
Squash (Dana)
Williams Sport (Williams Spain)

Smooth natural odours suit people who are sensitive, tender and dreamy, who do not want to force their character with an aggressive aroma. You need a perfume that does not clash with your great emotionality. If you are also romantic

and sentimental, you will find floral fragrances to your liking, smooth and delicate, without discordant notes and not at all compromising. Lavender suits men with the same traits.

Men

Country Man *(Mas)*
English Lavender
  (Atkinsons)
Lavanda *(Myrurgia)*
Lavanda Inglesa *(Gal)*
Lavande Royale
  (Legrain)
Moustache *(Rochas)*
Pour un Homme *(Caron)*

Women

Anaïs Anaïs *(Cacharel)*
Cardin *(Cardin)*
Clair de Jour *(Lanvin)*
Fleur à Fleur *(L'Oréal)*
Fleur de Fleurs *(Nina Ricci)*
Impress *(Kanebo)*
Jardins de Bagatelle *(Guerlain)*
L'Air du Temps *(Nina Ricci)*
Le Jardin *(Factor)*
Lovetime *(Visconti di Modrone)*
Moana Bouquet *(Puig)*
Shower Cologne Jasmine
  (Shiseido)
Tatiana *(v. Fürstenburg)*
Valentino *(Valentino)*
Vereda Fleur *(Parera)*
White Linen *(Lauder)*
White Shoulders *(Wyvan)*

If you are naturally bouncy, optimistic, pleasing, spontaneous and unaffected, citric fresh and green compositions will bring out these qualities.

Women

Agua Profonda (Parera)
Eau Courante (Rubinstein)
Eau Joya (Myrurgia)
Eau Folle (Laroche)
Espiègle (Atkinsons)
Farala (Gal)
Mademoiselle Ricci (Nina Ricci)
Variations (Carven)
Vent Vert (Balmain)

Men

Brando Splash (Parera)
Eau de Monsieur Balmain (Balmain)
Gentilhomme (Weil)
Green Water (J. Fath)
Lamborghini (Lamborghini)
Monsieur Lanvin (Lanvin)
Nino Cerutti (Roberre)
Signoricci (Nina Ricci)
Yerba Cologne (Puig)

The shy person, who is not very sure of himself or herself, prefers subdued aromas which are not too conspicuous in public. For the woman the most suitable are the floral notes; for men fresh fragrances which are lavender-based.

Women

Bleuor (Myrurgia)
Calobra (Copesca)
Diorissimo (Dior)
Estivalia (Puig)
Fleurs de Rocaille (Caron)
Graciela (M. Astor)
Laura Biagiotti (Biagiotti)
Wild Meadow (Shulton)

Men

Añeja Colonia (Gal)
Kölnisch Wasser Farina (Farina)
Moustache (Rochas)
Pour un Homme (Caron)
Royale Ambrée (Legrain)
YSL pour Hommes (Yves St Laurent)

A free, independent character prefers aromas which are up-to-date, unconventional, such as greens, ferns and chypre. The masculine notes of hide and tobacco are of interest to the assertive woman. Her sense of freedom does not limit her to a single perfume; she is actually better off changing. At night the oriental perfumes will attract her. The aromas of greens, tobaccos, hide, vetiver, wood and amber are the best suited for men.

Women

Agressif (Vera)
Ambush (Dana)
Balafre (Léonard)
Cabochard (Grès)
Coriandre (Couturier)
Charlie (Revlon)

Diva (Ungaro)
Givenchy III (Givenchy)
Intrigue (Yardley)
KL (Lagerfeld)
Miss Balmain (Balmain)
Mitsouko (Guerlain)
Shanida (Yardley)
Shocking (Schiaparelli)

Men

Agressif (Gal)
Andros (Parera)
Azzaro (Azzaro)
Brando Club (Parera)
Etienne Aignier Nr. 2 (Aignier)
Imperial Leather Classic (Cussons)
Kanon (Scannon)
Madras (Myrurgia)
Monsieur Givenchy (Givenchy)
Revillon pour Homme (Revlon)
Ted Lapidus (Lapidus)
Vetiver de Puig (Puig)
Yatagan (Caron)

If you are outgoing, sociable, restless, versatile, always ready to do lots of different things at the same time, you probably won't be faithful to one particular mark of perfume. Penetrating warm, sweet or sensual smells do not attract you. Your favourite fragrances are simple natural waters such as fern, wild and floral fresh aromas. Men will prefer dry and bitter variations.

Women

Dior-Dior (Dior)
Diorella (Dior)
Eau Fraîche (Léonard)
Janine D (4711)
Loewe (Loewe)
Moana Frappé (Puig)
K de Krizia (Krizia)

Men

Agua Brava (Puig)
Balafre (Lancôme)
Care (M. Astor)
Eau de Vétiver (Carven)
Eau de Vétiver (Guerlain)
Eau de Vétiver (Lanvin)

A person with natural charm, attractive manners and a capacity for being at ease in all circumstances, along with the power to impress, will like a warm perfume, with bitter notes of chypre and the orient, which will give a glimpse of a frivolous, teasing nature.

Women

Aphrodisia (Fabergé)
Azzaro (Azzaro)
Cachet (Matchabelli)
Calèche (Hermès)
Chant d'Arômes (Guerlain)
Embrujo de Sevilla (Myrurgia)
Gauloise (Molyneux)
Intimate (Revlon)
Lady 80 (Kanebo)
Ma Griffe (Carven)
Miss Dior (Dior)
Miss Worth (Worth)
Missoni (Missoni)
Parure (Guerlain)
Quadrille (Balenciaga)
Senchal (Charles of the Ritz)
The Female Factor (Factor)
Zambra (Puig)

Men

Eau pour Monsieur (Chanel)
Habit Rouge (Guerlain)
Santos (Cartier)

Are you kind, attentive and discreet? Use natural waters and fresh fragrances, fresh citric and floral which never offend nor annoy others. Men with this temperament ought to choose fresh and lavender-based aromas.

Women
Alada (Myrurgia)
Babe (Fabergé)
Eau de Givenchy (Givenchy)
Estivalia (Puig)
1916 (Myrurgia)
Tosca (4711)
Vereda (Parera)

Men
Eau Sauvage (Dior)
English Lavender (Yardley)
Grès pour Homme (Grès)
Juvena (Men)
Loewe pour Hommes (Loewe)
Patrichs (L. Philippe)

The elegant, distinguished, formal woman who loves beauty in all its forms, who is conservative, fixed in her ideas, and who dislikes having to take risks, will choose perfumes to enhance her character, such as those with an aldehyde florid harmony which will express her elegance to the fullest degree within the limits of classical perfumery. A man will find Chypre fragrances suitable for him as they are as robust as he is and do not lack natural freshness.

Women

Arpège (Lanvin)
Calandre (Rabanne)
Chanel 5 (Chanel)
Chicane (Jacomo)
Dorée (Puig)
Farouche (Nina Ricci)
Fashion (Léonard)
Flora Danica (Swank)
Infini (Caron)
Je Reviens (Worth)
Joya (Myrurgia)
Rive Gauche (Yves St Laurent)
Tamango (Léonard)

Men

Brummel (Williams Hispania)
Burberrys for Men (E. Arden)
Courrèges pour Hommes (Courrèges)
Etienne Aigner Nr. 1 (Aigner)
Ghibly (Atkinsons)
Gérard Danfre (G. Danfre)
Gucci pour Hommes (Gucci)
L'Homme (Roger Gallet)
Monsieur Rochas (Rochas)
Monsieur Worth (Worth)
Rothschild (Rothschild)
Sir Irisch Moss (4711)
That Man (Revlon)

If you like to be the centre of attention, if you are proud and extravagant, only the best and most novel are good enough for you. You are fond of wearing lots of perfume with oriental and spicy fragrances. These hot, rich perfumes tie in with your snobbism, because they are uncommon and very personal and give rise to many different comments. They will please your character.

Women

Amun (4711
Arrogance (Pikenz the First)
Bal à Versailles (Desprez)
Dioressence (Dior)
Gianni Versace (Versace)
J'ai osé (Laroche)
L'Atouche (El Corte Inglés)
L.A. (Factor)
Nocturnes (Caron)
Opium (Yves St Laurent)
Paris (Yves St Laurent)
Prélude (Balenciaga)
Sarabé (Juvena)
Vôtre (Jourdan)

Men

Antaeus (Chanel)
Jacomo (Jacomo)
Jovan Musk for Men (Jovan)
Kouros (Yves St Laurent)
Macassar (Rochas)
Men's Cologne (Cardin)
One Man Show (Bogart)
Patou pour Hommes (Patou)
Van Cleef and Arpels pour
*   Hommes (V. C. & A.)*

Is it your nature to be an individualist? If so, you will want unusual perfumes that are distinctive and unfamiliar. Modern tones, including green and fern, will suit your creative personality. Women of your disposition tend to like masculine aromas, such as tobacco and leather, while men of similar character tend to like rather flowery fragrances.

Women

Amérique (Courrèges)
Armani (Armani)
Bandit (Piguet)
Choc (Cardin)
Empreinte (Courrèges)
Folies Bergères (Caron)
Jean Louis Scherrer (J.L.S.)
Métal (Rabanne)
Paris (Yves St Laurent)
Quant (Quant)
Ravissa (M & W)
Scoundrel (Revlon)

Men

Aramis (Lauder)
Chiaro (Charles of the Ritz)
Drakkar Noir (Laroche)
Dunhill EdC (Dunhill)
Gérard Danfre Selection (G.D.)
Grey Flannel (G. Beene)
Halston 12 (Halston)
Kouros (Yves St Laurent)
Libero (Vera)
Macassar (Rochas)
Men's Style (Juvena)
Monsieur Jovan (Jovan)
Pour Lui (Oscar de la Renta)
Quorum (Puig)
Tabac Original (M & W)
Turbo (Fabergé)

If you are ambitious and strive for things, which you eventually obtain with patience and fixity of purpose, you will prefer insistent, conventional perfumes and modern florid warm tones. Men will go for the bitter and dry perfumes.

Women

Bellodgia (Caron)
Charles of the Ritz (Charles of the Ritz)
Joy (Patou)
L'Heure Bleue (Guerlain)
Maderas de Oriente (Myrurgia)
Michelle (Balenciaga)
Oscar de la Renta (Oscar de la Renta)
Vanderbilt (Vanderbilt)

Men

Brando (Parera)
Gentlemen (Givenchy)
Madrás (Myrurgia)
Masculin 2 (Bourjois)
Vétiver (Carven)
Yacaré (Astor)
Yachtman (Mas)

People know you to be a generous, magnanimous person. You will no doubt be attracted to oriental and spicy aromas. Men too will appreciate the more recent perfumes and, preferably, spicy notes.

Men

Cacherel pour Homme (Cacherel)
Eau Cendrée (Jacomo)
Equipage (Hermès)
Grès Monsieur (Grès)
Halston Z 14 (Halston)
Men (Mennen)
Monsieur Carven (Carven)
Musk (Mas)
Old Spice (Shulton)
Superfragrance for Men (Aigner)
Varón Dandy International (Parera)
Versailles pour Hommes (Desprez)

Women

Chimère (Prince Matchabelli)
Eau de Caron (Caron)
Emeraude (Coty)
Habanita (Molinard)
Le Dix (Balenciaga)
Must (Cartier)
Number Six (Betrix)
Sarabé (Juvena)
Tabu (Dana)
Vu (Lapidus)
Youth Dew (Lauder)

Energetic, active people who will do anything, can express their aggressivity and vitality when they choose a perfume. The adventurous daring spirit will drive them to find unknown perfumes, which excite their adventurous and impatient nature. Modern perfumes with a green bouquet suit their character. These fragrances are usually based on risqué bitter bottom notes. They are bold, but keep distances. They are dynamic without ceasing to be discreet. They do not make you dream, but they do stimulate the powers of imagination.

Women

Alliage (Lauder)
Cialenga (Balenciaga)
Chanel 19 (Chanel)
Givenchy III (Givenchy)
Graffiti (Capucci)
Oasis (Myrurgia)
Private Collection (Lauder)
Ravissa (M & W)
Silences (Jacomo)

Men

Agua Brava (Puig)
Blue Stratos (Shulton)
Drakkar (Laroche)
Grass Oil for Men (Jovan)
Monsieur Lanvin (Lanvin)
Nino Cerrutti (Cerutti)

Is your life full of commotion and devoted to the pursuit of pleasure? For the woman who always wants to be 'in', who dresses in the latest fashions, and never tires of discotheques, fresh, fruity and spicy aromas are the best. He will no doubt choose spicy, aromatic bitter, tobacco-musk scents.

Women

Armani (Armani)
Baruffa (Atkinsons)
Bill Blass (B. Blass)
Chloé (Lagerfeld)
Choc (Cardin)
David de Mas (Mas)
Diagonal (Puig)
Envoi (Lapidus)
First (V. C. & A.)
Halston Night (Halston)
Madame Carven (Carven)
Nahéma (Guerlain)
Paillettes (E. Coveri)
Paradoxe (Cardin)
Paris (Yves St Laurent)
Tendance (Marbert)
Trussardi (Trussardi)

Men

Andros (Parera)
Bogart (Bogart)
Calvin (Calvin Klein)
Flint (Boots)
Gérard Danfre Sélection (G. D.)
Gilvan (Kanebo)
Paco Rabanne pour Homme (Rabanne)
Portos (Balenciaga)
Pour Lui (Oscar de la Renta)
Punjab (Capucci)
Quorum (Puig)
Trussardi (Trussardi)

Most suited to the work-aholic, tidy-minded person, who is also established and orderly, are natural and fresh, woody or country fragrances which are devoid of sensual tones.

Women

Amazone (Hermès)
Eau de Lancaster (Lancaster)
Eau Fraîche de Léonard
(Léonard)
4711 (4711)
Quartz (Molyneux)
Tempo (Avon)
Vereda (Parera)

Men

Aqua Manda (Goya)
Dollars (E. Coveri)
Herbal (Aramis)
Hurlingham (Atkinsons)
Pino Silvestre (Vidal)
Pyn's Colonia (Parera)
Signor (Victor)
Silvestre (Victor)

If you are affectionate and understanding, floral, aldehydic, spicy, wood aromas will enhance your personality. Men will appreciate spicy, bitter, tobacco, hide and lavender aromas.

Men

Admiral's Yachtman (Mas)
Avon Lavender (Avon)
Blend 30 (Dunhill)
Eau de Lavanda (4711)
Lucky (Mas)
Royal Copenhagen (Swank)
Sandalwood (Arden for Men)
Tabac Original (M & W)
Varón Dandy (Parera)

Women

Anna Vera (Vera)
Antilope (Weil)
Capricci (Nina Ricci)
Detchema (Revillon)
Estée (Lauder)
Fidji (Laroche)
Flamme (Bourjois)
Guirlandes (Carven)
Hanorable (Hanorah)
L'Aimant (Coty)
L'Air du Temps (Nina Ricci)
Le de (Givenchy)
Première (4711)

Natural, green, tobacco, hide and fern (fougère) aromas are recommended for the intellectual, who does not like warm and inebriating perfumes.

Women

Ainsi (Atkinsons)
Aromatic Elixir (Clinique)
Jolie Madame (Balmain)
Oasis (Myrurgia)
Zany (Avon)

Men

Agresste (Gal)
Brut (Fabergé)
Eau de Cologne Impériale
   (Guerlain)
Country Man (Mas)
Heno de Pravia (Gal)
Old Brown (Parera)

Cautious and disciplined? Then conventional, lingering fragrances and florid warm perfumes of today will reflect your faithful character. Bitter and dry notes bestow these qualities on a man.

Women
Joy (Patou)
Madame Rochas (Rochas)
Oasis (Myrurgia)
Soir de Paris (Bourjois)
Vanderbilt (Vanderbilt)

Men
Gentlemen (Givenchy)
Off Shore (Victor)
Vetiver (Bogart)
Vetyver (Roger & Gallet)

The seducer, the sensual and passionate person will reflect his deep emotions with intoxicating perfumes based on the lily, hyacinth, tuberose, rose, jasmine and spikenard. Flowery bitter, powdery and oriental compositions with the animal tones of amber, musk and civet, which exude mystery and passion are their favourite aromas. Oriental and musky chords are recommended for him.

Men

J. H. L. (Lauder)
Jules (Dior)
Kouros (Yves St Laurent)
Lagerfeld (Lagerfeld)
Léonard pour Homme
  (Léonard)
Macho Musk (Fabergé)
Musk for Men (Avon)
Musk for Men (Yardley)
Oriental Eastern Spice
  (Shulton)

Women

Aquamarine (Revlon)
Blue Grass (Arden)
Chamode (Guerlain)
Cinnabar (Lauder)
Chloé (Lagerfeld)
Femme (Rochas)
Fête (Molyneux)
Le Temps d'Aimer (A. Delon)
Maja (Myrurgia)
Miocha (Christian Gray)
Moment Suprême (Patou)
Moon Drops (Revlon)
Ombre Rose (Brosseau)
Opium (Yves St Laurent)
Shalimar (Guerlain)

As other minds sail
on the crest of music
mine floats
on the waves of your perfume

Baudelaire

Depósito legal B. 9209-1985
Grafos S.A. 08013 Barcelona